I'M HAPPY-SAD TODAY

Making Sense of Mixed-Together Feelings

Lory Britain, Ph.D.

Illustrated by Matthew Rivera

SCHOLASTIC INC.

ISBN 978-1-338-64696-2

13 12   21 22 23 24 25

Printed in the U.S.A.   40

First Scholastic printing, January 2020

Edited by Alison Behnke
Cover and interior design by Emily Dyer

Thanks and gratitude to my wonderful, older granddaughter and editor, Momo, for telling me one afternoon that she was "SMAD" and inspiring me to write this book. And with much appreciation for my amazing younger granddaughter, Eliana, who shares her big ideas and big feelings with me.

Sometimes I just feel **happy** . . . that's all!

I feel the "noisy, giggly, jump and run" kind of happy.

Sometimes, I feel a different kind of **happy**.

When I'm cozy in my favorite spot
with my favorite book,
I'm the quiet kind of happy.

Other times, I feel **sad**.

Once I was sick and couldn't go
to my friend's birthday party.

I had a "crying, nothing's right" sort of sad.

The day our neighbors moved away,
I was a different kind of **sad**.

I didn't smile for that whole day
or even part of the next day.

Lots of times, I have more than one feeling inside of me.

Like when my mom picks me up at school and I have to stop playing.
I'm **happy** to see her, but **sad** to leave my friends.

I say, "Mom, I'm **happy-sad** together!"

WORD WALL

Apple	Father	Blue
Cloud	Banana	Dream
Dime	Dish	Chicken

WHOOO'S HELPER OF THE WEEK?

Jayden

DINO-MITE!

CLASSROOM JOBS

The morning I walked into my new
classroom for the very first time,
I felt **scared** and **brave** together.

Lots of people feel that way sometimes.

Last week, I was **friendly** and **shy** at once.

I felt too shy to talk to the new girl
even when I gave her a friendly smile.

Sometimes, I feel **nervous** and **excited** at the same time.
That's how I felt about my first sleepover.

I was nervous for two whole days before it was time to go—
and excited too!

One time, I had two big feelings swirling around inside.

I was **sad** and **mad** when my friends wouldn't play with me.
I felt sad that they weren't being nice . . .
and mad they didn't let me play.

Both feelings together!

When I fell down at the playground,
I wasn't sure how I felt or what I wanted.

Part of me wanted to be picked up like a little kid.
Another part of me wanted to get right up and keep climbing!

I had a **little kid feeling** and a **big kid feeling** mixed together.

I had big feelings when my baby brother was born.

I was **proud** to be a big sister.

And I was **jealous** of all the attention he was getting.

I had proud and jealous feelings inside of me.

That was confusing.

Last week, I learned to cut out a circle with scissors.
I couldn't cut a curvy line on my first try.
I was **frustrated**.

I didn't want any help.
I was **determined** to keep trying.

Finally, I did it!

When I have more than one
feeling inside of me,

I don't have to choose just one.

I know that all my feelings
are okay at the same time.

If I want to, I can tell my friend about my feelings.

Or I can tell a grown-up about all my feelings.
I can say what happened and how I feel.

Sometimes I don't even have to talk.
I can just be with someone and feel better.

Sometimes when my feelings are mixed together,
I like to **pretend**.

I can pretend my animals
have the same feelings I do.

I can **dance** and **swirl** around,
just like my feelings swirl inside of me.

Moving helps me feel better.

I can even **paint** two pictures at the same time to show those together feelings!

Shappy

Smad

Worry s

I make up my own words for my
together feelings sometimes.

If I am **sad** and **mad** together,
I can say, "I'm **smad**."

Or if I am feeling **shy** and **happy**,
I say, "I'm **shappy**!"

I can make up a lot of pretend feeling words.

And do you know what?

When I'm older, sometimes I'll still have different
feelings mixed together inside of me.

Happcited

Hapsad

Braverous

Glappy

Scited

Loveappy

And that's okay!

Talking and Learning About Feelings: A Guide for Caring Adults

Young children often face challenging and even conflicting feelings—just as adults do. And—just as they can be for adults—these feelings can be confusing and difficult to handle. For kids, these emotions might arise during common childhood situations such as a first-time sleepover or starting school, or during serious and difficult situations involving worry, trauma, or abuse. *I'm Happy-Sad Today* helps children begin to understand and express their complex, mixed-together feelings without having to choose one feeling over another. Whether you're a teacher, a parent, or other adult, you can use this book as a starting point to help children develop essential skills for expressing all their feelings today and in the future.

How to Read This Book with Children

As you read and discuss this book, be responsive to children by validating what they share and by matching your pace, remarks, and questions to their comments. Be attentive to their body language, pausing to give them opportunities to share their thoughts. Be sensitive to how and when children want to share about their feelings.

Sometimes children will want to listen to you read this book from beginning to end without interruption. Or children might be interested in hearing the book read from beginning to end, with frequent pauses for discussion. You might also choose to focus on only one or two pages at a time, allowing children to share similar feelings that are sparked by the pictures and words.

Whether you include discussion during the reading or at the end, ask open-ended questions and offer comments to encourage children to go deeper into their feelings and experiences, and to validate the importance of their feelings. Here are some examples.

- "That might be confusing sometimes. Thank you for sharing about all your feelings."
- "How did you feel when you went to a new friend's home for the first time?"

- "Tell me about a time you also felt nervous and excited at once."
- "What feelings do you have when you try something new?"
- "Sometimes I also feel excited and then I feel shy when I _____."
- "What feelings do you feel when you _____?"

Remember, open-ended questions and comments encourage children to go deeper to process and express their feelings and experiences. For example, consider the difference between asking a child, "Do you feel sad?" and saying, "I am interested in hearing about all the feelings you are having right now," or "Tell me about how you are feeling now." The first closed-ended question may only elicit a "yes" or "no" response, while the second approach is more likely to result in children sharing specific feelings and why they feel that way.

As you discuss feelings with children, keep in mind that while multiple emotions can sometimes occur at the same moment, there are other times when many different feelings might come in quick succession. Children, like adults, may be caught off guard by this cascade of feelings. And sometimes, one feeling can mask or hide another feeling. Also remember that children may not show their feelings through facial expressions, even when they are experiencing strong emotions.

Note: During a group reading, if a child divulges information about a serious issue such as violence or abuse, validate their feelings, thank them for sharing, and arrange to listen to the child later in an appropriate way and place. Also be sure that you are aware of policies in your program, school, or district about reporting this type of information.

Strategies for Supporting Children's Social-Emotional Development

Model Self-Expression

As adults, our words, actions, and body language are a powerful way of conveying to children values and ways of being in the world. When you are struggling to unlatch a cabinet, for example, you might say, "I feel frustrated that this is stuck, but I am determined to get it open." You are giving children the implicit message that a person can have more than one feeling at once.

Encourage Children to Express Themselves with Words

Encourage children to share about all their feelings using their words. Help them learn and know accurate names for their feelings, and guide them to use these words even when their feelings are running high. Your body language, including being at the child's level and eye contact, is also a form of encouragement. Allowing for unrushed, relaxed time together creates an environment conducive to talking and sharing.

Validate and Reinforce

Validate children's words and actions by saying, "Thank you for sharing all your big [or deep] feelings with me." This focus on multiple feelings sends the message that all feelings are okay, including when they happen at the same time. Remember to help children separate their feelings from their actions and understand that while all feelings are acceptable, all actions are not. One example might be to say, "All of your feelings are okay to have, but it is *not* okay to hit."

Consider the Current Situation

If you feel a child needs particular support, evaluate the physical environment and what is happening in it. Are other children waiting at the door to go outside or trying to get their coats on? Is a baby crying and in need of timely care? Also consider the emotional receptiveness and physical status of the child who needs emotional support. Is the child tired or hungry? Perhaps the child wants comforting touches before even starting to talk about feelings. These considerations and more will guide you as you think about how to best support children in the moment. Depending on the situation, you may want to offer a quick, friendly response and check in again with the child later, or you may take the time to offer more support right away.

Also remember to "seize the moment." Be attentive to a child's words and body language in a given moment and try to support that child's immediate needs. For example, suppose a parent says to you, "Alicia's favorite aunt will be picking her up from school today." You sense from Alicia's body language that she might be a bit anxious about this. After the parent leaves, consider Alicia's immediate emotional receptiveness to discussion. If she is really upset, a hug or soft shoulder touch might be more appropriate than words. Or perhaps walking over to a classroom feeling chart or pulling out this book (or another book on feelings) would best support Alicia. Again, you will still need to consider the specifics of the moment. For example, if you have three children standing nearby who are waiting to wash finger paint off their hands, it may be most realistic to make a simple, supportive statement to Alicia and then follow up with her in a more substantial way later.

Encourage Kids to Think About How Others Feel

Becoming emotionally aware also means learning to understand the perspective of others and accept all the feelings other people may have. It means reflecting on how actions and circumstances affect others. During a challenging interaction between two children, consider using questions and comments to develop this awareness and understanding. For example, if one child excludes another, you might say, "I am wondering how José feels when you won't play with him," or "What feelings do you think Bai has right now?" or "Rosie, can you tell Ahmad how you are feeling right now?"

Plan Ahead

Planning ahead can be an important part of helping children reach deeper to share about all their feelings. The following two ideas give you ways to set the stage for these discussions.

- In strategic areas where children will see them often, place feeling charts and pictures of children engaged in activities. Effective spots to choose could include near a classroom door, near a child's bed, or near an eating area. Regularly invite and encourage children to select all of their feelings on the feeling chart. Or guide children to look at the pictures and discuss how the children in the pictures might be feeling. Remember to select pictures and drawings that are understandable to children and represent all types of diversity (including gender, ethnicity, body types, and physical abilities).

- Always have a range of age-appropriate and diverse books easily accessible to children, and be open to using them as jumping-off points for conversation. Remember that books about complex emotions do not have to be limited to books that *specifically* discuss or focus on emotions. Books conveying childhood experiences and events in their lives often elicit comments and discussions about multiple feelings. Some of the most poignant stories are those that resonate with children's emotions around a singular childhood circumstance, such as going to bed, losing a pet, going to the doctor, or having a new friend. Also have books that address delicate subjects, such as divorce or domestic violence, readily available for adults to select and read privately with an individual child.

Incorporate Sharing Feelings into Problem-Solving

When problem-solving with a child or group of children, help them express and represent all their feelings during the problem-solving process. Often sharing feelings is the first step before generating possible solutions to a problem. Remember that following through after implementing a solution could involve sharing about feelings again. For example, after children choose and implement a solution to a game-sharing problem and play together, facilitate a follow-up discussion for children to share their feelings about the results.

Share These Concepts with Caring Adults in Children's Lives

Support consistency in children's lives by sharing the ideas in this book with classroom helpers, co-teachers, volunteers, family members, and other caring adults. Whether in a classroom or home, consistency supports children's emotional development.

More Ideas for Activities and Discussion

All these activities draw on ideas in *I'm Happy-Sad Today* but some relate directly to moments in the story. In those cases, you'll see page numbers referencing the relevant spot in the book.

Telling a Caring Adult (page 23)

Encourage children to tell adults about their feelings, and discuss ideas for who they might go to when they need or want to talk. If you are one of the adults children come to, remember that listening to a child means more than hearing his or her words. Put your body at the child's level and remember that eye contact and other body language convey your emotional presence. And being present for a child doesn't always involve words. Sometimes offering a lap or hug is just what is needed to help a child begin to sort out feelings.

Using Words with Friends (page 22)

Help children become comfortable using their words to tell their friends about all their feelings. Offer verbal prompts to encourage children to use their words and to take turns talking and listening. For example, "Hector, what words can you use to tell Melissa how you are feeling?" or "Clara said she is feeling lonely. How can you help her feel better?"

Pretending with Animals, Dolls, or Little Figures (page 24)

Create a "feeling" basket with multiple sets of toys, figures, or dolls representing animals and people. Encourage children to manipulate the animals and people to talk about all their feelings. Encourage acting out the various scenes in the book with animals, people, and puppets, or guide older children in role-play.

Dancing and Movement (page 26)

You can plan for this experience by selecting assorted musical recordings to represent different feelings for children to express through dance and movement. Ask them to describe their feelings when they move to the music.

Painting (page 27)

Set out two pieces of paper on a desk, a table, or an easel, and make paints and brushes available. (Alternatively, you could use crayons or colored pencils.) Suggest that children pick different colors and use both hands at the same time to create art representing their mixed-together feelings. Consider playing selected music from the dancing activity during painting. Materials such as modeling clay and finger paints also lend themselves to depict different emotions.

Making Up Words (page 28)

Although complex emotions can be serious or challenging at times, adding a bit of humor now and then—depending on the situation—can enhance emotional awareness and help children be more receptive to learning experiences. Children delight in combining feeling words to come up with new words, such as "smad" or "shappy." Get creative! For example, children may enjoy thinking of a way their favorite food could represent their complex or mixed-together feelings through words like "macaroni-fied" or "mashy-potatoey."

Twirling Feeling Faces

Create feeling faces by attaching wooden stick handles to paper plates (or having children do so). Next have children draw a different feeling face on each side of the paper plate. Children can make multiple sets and use the feeling faces to twirl from side to side to express all their feelings.

Puppet of Many Feelings

Draw different simple faces on the fingers of a pair of adult-sized cloth gloves to represent emotions of your choice, or use small printed emotion faces and attach them to the glove fingers. Use these puppets at relevant times to encourage children to point out how they're feeling.

Basket of Cards

Choose five to ten emotions and create at least two matching cards depicting each one (using photocopies of magazine cutouts, for example). Place them in a shallow basket or box for visibility. Instead of a typical matching game, play a "Different Feelings Together" game with children. Invite a child to suggest a scenario that might provoke mixed feelings, such as "My friend sat with someone else on the bus today." Next, have that child choose as many cards as desired to represent all the feelings he or she would have in that situation and place them face-up on a table or other surface. You could then have a second child choose a new scenario and start over, *or* you could invite other children to select or point to cards that show how they would feel in the situation.

Another way to use these cards is to place them face-down on a table or other surface and have children take turns flipping over two cards. Leaving the cards turned over, ask the child to name the feelings he or she sees and talk about when those feelings might happen together. The next child who takes a turn could then do the same thing. As more cards are turned over, children could also talk about when they might feel these combinations of feelings.

Story and Discussion Starters

Prepare a file box with large pictures of a child or children engaged in an activity and/or displaying emotions. (Again, include all types of diversity within these pictures.) Use these pictures to stimulate discussion or as progressive story starters. For story starters, show a picture and say something like, "Once there was a little boy [or girl] who _____." Ask children to fill in the blanks. After a child contributes, move the story along. For example, you might say, "Next, he wanted to _____." Or, "He had many feelings that day. His feelings were _____ and _____." Continue the story with this pattern, taking the lead from children's responses.

Making Music from Feelings

Offer instruments to children and invite them to make music that they feel represents all the feelings they are feeling at once. Record each child's music and words and play these recordings for children. You might ask questions like, "What mixed-together feelings would you like to share about?" or "What feelings do you have when you hear this music?"

Other Feeling Activities

There are many other wonderful activities you can use to help children focus on, express, cope with, and accept their feelings. Brainstorm with others about how you can expand common games and activities to focus on the concepts from *I'm Happy-Sad Today*. For example, you could change the lyrics "If you're happy and you know it, clap your hands" to "If you're happy and you're angry, clap your hands and stomp your feet" or "use your words." (You can ask children to suggest the new emotions and actions.) Enjoy continuing to find new and creative ways to explore emotions with children!

Through open discussion, consistent support, and gentle guidance, you can help children understand that it's perfectly okay to have more than one feeling at once. This powerful understanding is a gift that will stay with them throughout their lives.

About the Author and Illustrator

Lory Britain, Ph.D., has more than forty years of experience working with children, teachers, and families. Her background includes time in the classroom as a preschool teacher; helping found therapeutic child and family programs; teaching undergraduate and graduate courses in early childhood education; and presenting at state, national, and international conferences for professionals who work with young children. In addition to this work, Dr. Britain has written many children's books that help kids stay safe and express their feelings and ideas. She also takes her therapy dog, Puppet, to visit children in hospitals and schools. Lory lives in Eugene, Oregon.

Matthew Rivera is an award-winning illustrator from Los Angeles. He graduated from the University of Arizona with a bachelor's degree in fine arts, then moved to Los Angeles where he worked as an art director for agencies, large corporations, and toy companies. Now he makes art and writes stories for kids. He is happiest making art, eating French fries, and exploring his city.